JONAH

Tammar Stein

Sabina Hahn

Library of Congress Control Number
2021950838

Designed by Sabina Hahn

First Edition
10 9 8 7 6 5 4 3 2 1
0822/B1896/A7
Printed in China

CHAPTER ONE

Meet Jonah

Jonah was a teacher.

Back in those days, there were no school buildings. Jonah sat under the shade of a tree, and his students sat on the ground in front of him.

Jonah's students loved his class. They loved the stories he told. They enjoyed the snacks of figs and raisins he brought for them.

Jonah was a great teacher, and he loved his students. But sometimes they were naughty. We all make bad choices sometimes.

One day, a student poked another student with a stick.

"That was not okay," Jonah scolded. "Would you like it if someone poked you with a stick?"

The student realized he would not like that at all. He felt badly about hurting his friend. He apologized and asked for forgiveness. The children made up. The class continued.

CHAPTER TWO

Go

God saw that Jonah was a good teacher.
God saw that when Jonah scolded his students,
they really listened.

God said to Jonah, "The people of Nineveh have been
wicked. If they don't change their ways, I will have
to punish them. You must go there and warn them."
"Who, me?" Jonah asked.
"Yes, you," God said.

Jonah didn't want to go to a wicked city.
He didn't want to scold the people there.
What if they laughed at him?
What if they yelled at him?
What if they attacked him?

"Go!" God said.

Jonah went.
But not to Nineveh.

He ran to the port.
He found a ship sailing
in the opposite direction.
He bought a ticket.

CHAPTER THREE
Running Away

The sailors raised the sail. The wind blew, and
the ship pulled away from the port. Soon, there
was only water as far as anyone could see.

Jonah breathed a sigh of relief.

The sailors on the ship had different
religions and different favorite foods than
Jonah. Even though Jonah was different,
the sailors were kind to him.

"Why are you on the ship?" they asked.
"I'm running away from God," Jonah said.
The sailors looked at each other.
They looked at Jonah.
"Good luck with that," they said.

That night, the ship rocked on gentle waves.
The stars twinkled overhead. Jonah lay on
the deck and looked at the dark sky.

Had he really managed it?
Had he really escaped from God?

CHAPTER FOUR

The Storm

The next morning, the waves were huge.

"It's a storm!" the sailors yelled.

"It came out of nowhere."

The storm grew worse and worse.

"This isn't a normal storm!"
they shouted. "Someone's
god is punishing us."

"Uh-oh," Jonah said.

The ship tilted, and everyone
fell. They had to hold on to
the ropes and the railing.
Everyone was in
danger because
of Jonah.

"This is all my fault!" Jonah shouted.
"Throw me overboard!"

"We can't do that."

"You have to!" Jonah yelled.
"It's the only way to save the ship."

The sailors threw Jonah into the water.
The wind stopped. The waves stopped.
The sea was soft and flat. The storm was over.

CHAPTER FIVE

The Whale

The water closed over Jonah's head.
It was cold. The sea was deep.
Jonah could not swim.

God, please save me, Jonah thought.
I shouldn't have run away. Please,
give me another chance.

At that moment, a large, dark shape
swam up under Jonah. It was a whale.
It had come from the bottom of the sea.

The whale opened its mouth.
It was as big as a door.

Down went Jonah.

Into the whale's mouth.

Down its throat.

Into its belly.

It was as big as a cave.
It was dark.
It was very smelly.

Jonah felt scared. What would happen to him?
Jonah felt angry. Why was this happening to him?
Jonah felt sorry. He had made some very bad decisions.

CHAPTER SIX

A Second Chance

Jonah spent three days and three nights inside
the whale. It gave him a lot of time to think.
He thought about what he had done.
He thought about what he should do.

"If you give me a second chance," Jonah
promised God, "I will go to Nineveh."

God decided Jonah was ready for a second chance.

The whale swam near the shore. The whale started throwing up. Up came everything in the whale's stomach: The fish it had eaten. The seaweed it had swallowed. And Jonah.

Jonah crawled onto the beach and flopped on the sand. He was alive. He was on dry land. He was slimy, but very happy.

Jonah got to his feet. He had a job to do.

CHAPTER SEVEN

Nineveh

Nineveh was a big city. It took three days to walk from one end to the other. Jonah felt nervous. But those long days and nights inside the whale had taught Jonah a lot. Even though he was scared, he still had to try.

"People of Nineveh!" he shouted. "You have been wicked!" Everyone stopped and stared.

"You have cheated your customers!" he yelled. "You have hit your animals. You have stolen and lied. God is angry with you. You will be punished."

Jonah's words scared
people. Some began to cry.
They apologized to each
other for the mean things
they had done. They prayed
God would forgive them and
give them a second chance.

The king of Nineveh
heard about Jonah
and his warning.

"We must all fast,"
the king announced.
"No one may eat or
drink. We must show
God how sorry we
are. We shall not
be wicked again."

CHAPTER EIGHT

Not Fair

For forty days, the people of Nineveh prayed
for forgiveness. They stopped cheating their
customers. They stopped hitting their animals.
They stopped stealing and telling lies.

Instead, they helped little old ladies cross the
street. They gave food to the poor and extra
treats to their animals.

God could have caused an earthquake to destroy the city. God could have made a big flood to wash them all away. But God saw they were sorry. They were making good choices now. God forgave them. The people of Nineveh were happy and grateful.

Jonah was not happy.

"This isn't fair," he said. "I had to leave my city and my students. I was on a boat in a storm. I almost drowned. I was swallowed by a horrible, smelly whale. I was stuck inside it for three days. Yet these wicked people say 'sorry' and aren't punished at all."

He stomped off, away from the city.

"It's not fair," he muttered. "If God was just going to forgive them, why bother with me?"

Jonah sat down at the top of a
nearby hill with a view of Nineveh.
He crossed his arms over his chest.
Jonah was angry at God.

CHAPTER NINE

The Vine and the Worm

God saw Jonah's feelings. God wanted
to help. God made a vine grow next
to Jonah. The vine grew quickly.

Within a day, the vine had grown big green leaves
and bright, beautiful flowers, and had curved up
and over Jonah. Now, Jonah had a nice, shady
spot. Jonah felt some of his anger melt away.
He relaxed, enjoying the beauty of his vine.

The next day, God sent a worm to eat
the vine. The green leaves turned yellow,
then brown. The vine shriveled up and
died. Jonah was in the hot sun again.

"This is awful!" Jonah cried.

"This is unfair! My poor vine!"

"Why are you upset?" God asked.

"You didn't make it. You didn't plant it.
You didn't even water it."

Jonah paused his crying.

"It grew in one day," God went on. "It left
the next day. What's the big deal?"

"But I loved that vine," Jonah said, quietly.

"And I love my people," God said, quietly.

CHAPTER TEN
Life Lessons

A cloud drifted over the sun. The day cooled.
Somewhere, a bird called out. Jonah nodded his
head. Now he understood. God made the world. God
loved everything and everyone in it. The people of
Nineveh were trying hard to live good lives. They
deserved their second chance. Jonah remembered
that God had given him a second chance, too.

Jonah returned to his city and his students. From that day on, Jonah taught them to remember three things.

One: Apologize when you make a bad choice.

Two: Take care of each other.

Three: Whales are great, but surprisingly smelly.